This
Book
Belongs
To _

Grolier Enterprises Inc.
SHERMAN TURNPIKE, DANBURY, CONNECTICUT 06816

Book Club Edition

The STORY Of The TOWER Of BABEL

An ALICE IN BIBLELAND® Storybook

Written by Alice Joyce Davidson
Designed by Victoria Marshall

A little girl named Alice
Was playing on the beach.
She built a big sand tower
Just as high as she could reach.

She rested for a while
Underneath a shady spot,
And read a Bible story
That she liked an awful lot.

As she read about a tower
That reached into the sky,
The airmail bird delivered
This note as he flew by:

"Reading is the magic key
To take you where you want to be."

The book that Alice held became
A very special screen.
She walked on through to Bibleland
And came upon this scene.

Noah's family had children,
And they had children, too.
Their grandchildren had children,
And the family grew and grew.

There were cousins by the dozen,
By the thousands, even more,
And with each year the family grew
Still bigger than before.

They spoke a single language,
And they understood each other
As well as any sister
Could understand her brother.

They roamed around the desert
Until they found a place one day,
A valley they called Shinar,
And thought they'd like to stay.

"We'll build a city," they agreed,
"The finest to be found.
For bricks, we'll use the orange clay,
There's plenty in the ground.

"And in the center, let us build
A tower very high.
It will reach clear up to heaven
Through the clouds high in the sky.

"We'll be famous for our tower
In this and every nation.
We'll be known throughout the ages
Through every generation.

"And when our name is famous,
Then we can live together
Beneath our glorious tower
Forever and forever."

So all the men and women
And their children worked all day.
They built a real fine city
Out of bricks they baked of clay.

But instead of acting thankful
For the blessings God had given,
They boasted of their tower
That would be as high as heaven.

And as the tower grew and grew,
They acted vain and proud.
They held their noses in the air
And bragged a lot out loud.

"We understand each other.
We work and speak as one.
We'll all be very famous
When our great big tower's done.

"We're wonderful, we're marvelous.
Together we have power,
And we'll be as high as heaven
When we're finished with our tower!"

The people worked together
Brick by brick and row by row.
In every kind of weather
They watched their tower grow.

God saw their prideful, boastful ways
As they worked up on the tower.
Because they spoke the same language,
The people felt their power.

And all that they imagined,
God worried they would do.
And if He didn't interfere,
Their vain scheme might come true.

So God spoke to all His angels,
And this was His command:
"Let's mix up the language
That's spoken in this land."

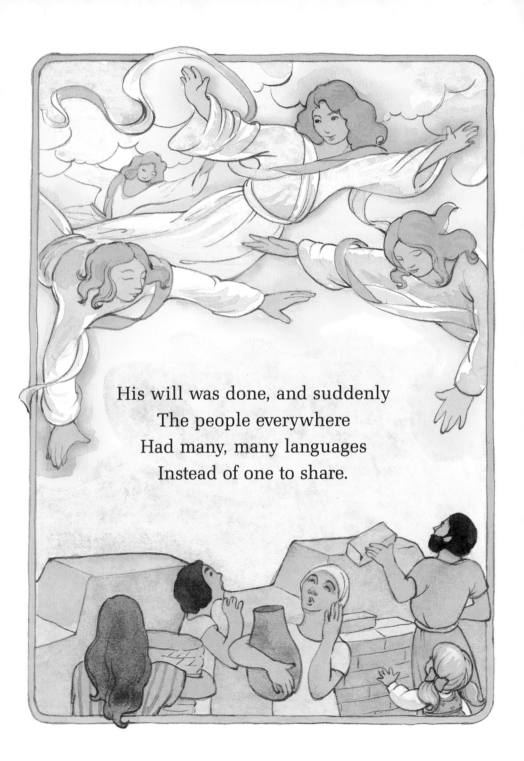

His will was done, and suddenly
The people everywhere
Had many, many languages
Instead of one to share.

"De bricka, ricka," one man said,
Which meant, "I want more bricks."
Someone scratched his head and gave
The man some broken sticks.

The women baking bricks heard wrong,
And started making bread.
The boys who carried water
All took a bath instead.

Great confusion filled the land.
It didn't take an hour
Before the builders had to stop
Working on the tower.

They couldn't work together.
Their scheme had come undone,
For God gave them many languages
Instead of only one.

The city was called Babel,
And today that is the word
That's used when there's confusion;
Or mixed up words are heard.

God spoke to His angels
And gave them this command,
"Let the people there be scattered,
Let them live in many lands."

The time had come for Alice
To leave that Bible scene.
So she returned from Bibleland
By walking through her screen.

She came back to her tower,
And put her book away.
And Alice thought, "I learned a lot
In Bibleland today.

"When we're blessed to have power,
We should use it not for fame,
Not for pride, and not for glory
Just to have a famous name.

"We should use our blessings
In good and loving ways,
And God will smile on us
With more blessings for our days."